Usborne

Dress the Teddy Bears Sticker Book

Felicity Brooks

Designed by Katrina Fearn

Illustrated by Ag Jatkowska

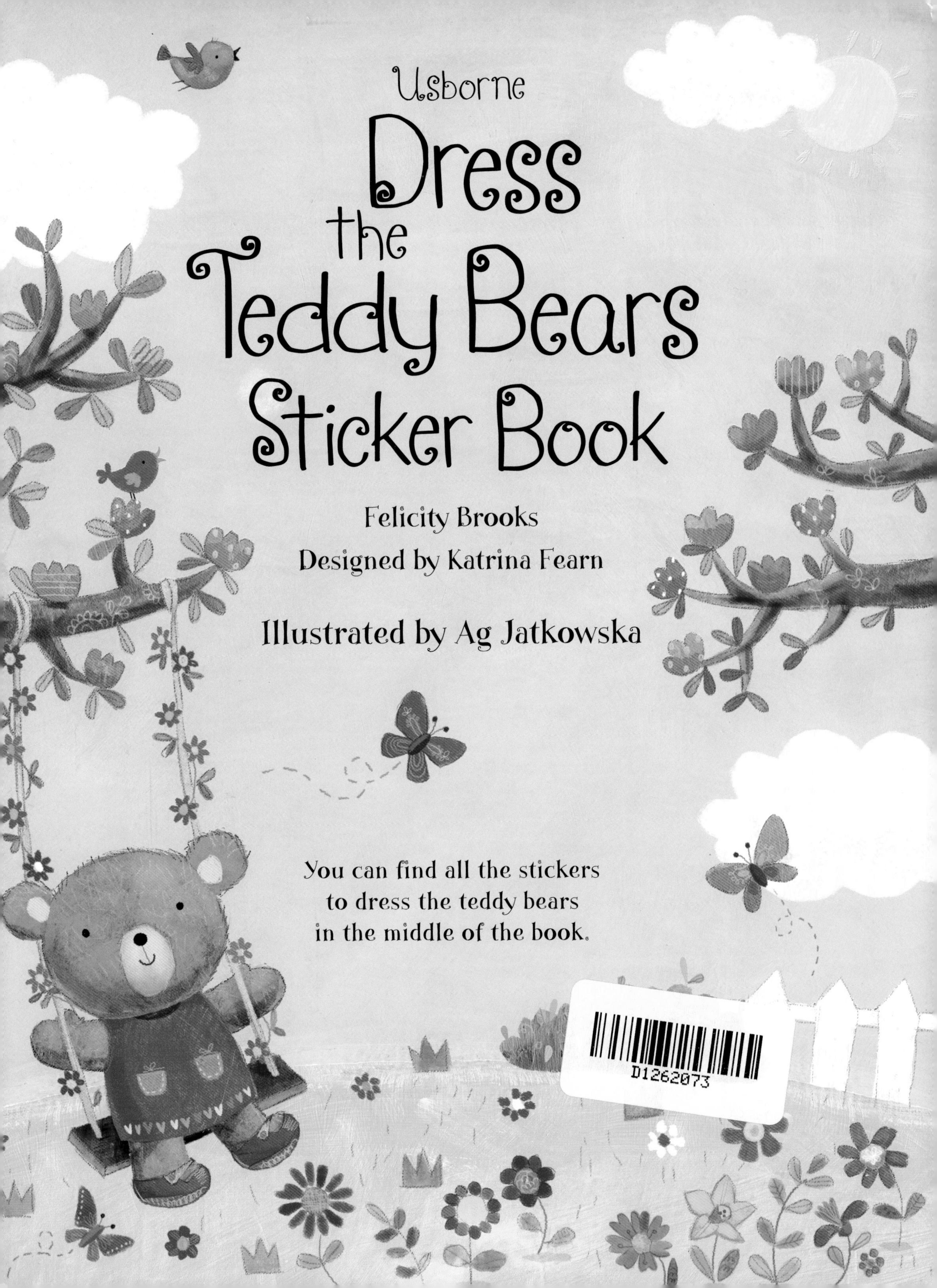

You can find all the stickers
to dress the teddy bears
in the middle of the book.

Say hello to the bears

These teddy bear friends live in a cozy little home in the forest. Say hello and choose some clothes to help them get ready for a busy day.

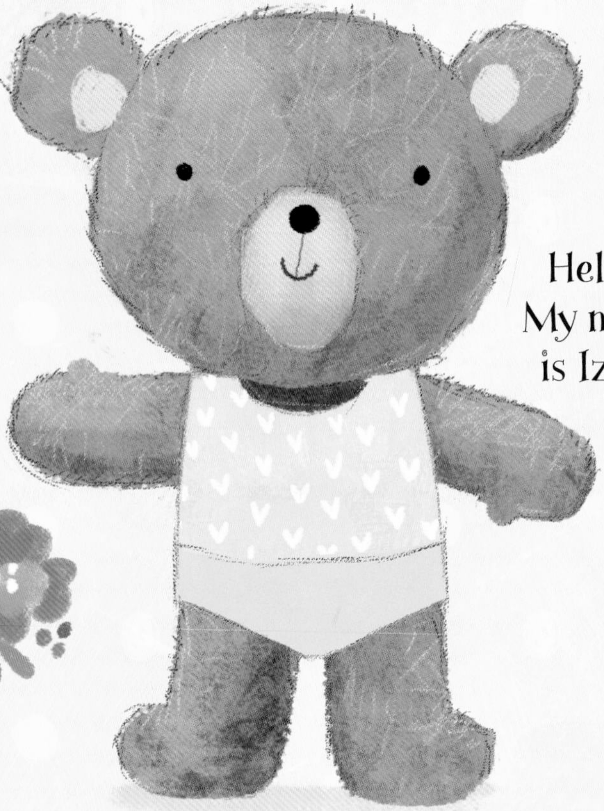

Hello!
My name
is Izzy.

Hello!
I'm Milly.

Izzy

Quiet and kind.
Likes singing and playing.
Loves white chocolate.
Favorite color: yellow.

Milly

Cheerful and brave.
Likes climbing trees.
Loves juicy red apples.
Favorite color: pink.

Hello!
I'm Oscar.

Hello!
My name is
Benjamin.

Oscar

Big and happy.
Likes dancing.
Loves honey sandwiches.
Favorite color: green.

Benjamin

Funny and messy.
Likes drawing and stories.
Loves cupcakes.
Favorite color: blue.

Going shopping

Today the bears are going to get some things they need to make a picnic, but it's raining. What can they wear to splash in the puddles?

pitter patter

splosh,
splish

Baking cakes

Back at home, the bears get busy baking cakes for the picnic. Can you find some cooking clothes for them to put on?

Hmmm,
cakes.
Yum!

The teddy bears' picnic

At last the sun has come out and the bears are having a picnic. Find some clothes for them to wear in the hot sun.

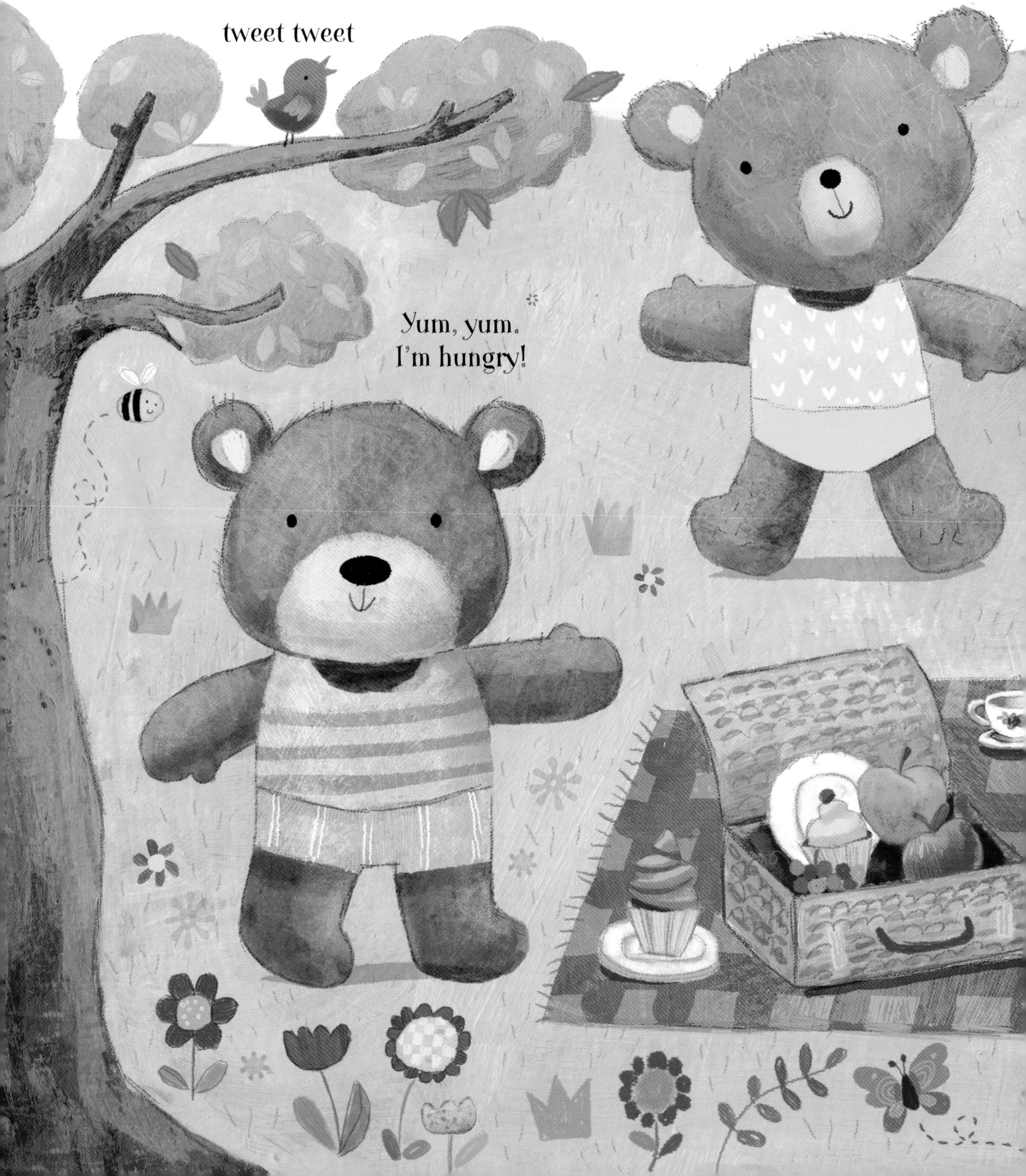
tweet tweet
Yum, yum.
I'm hungry!

Say hello to the bears

Going shopping

Benjamin

Milly

Oscar

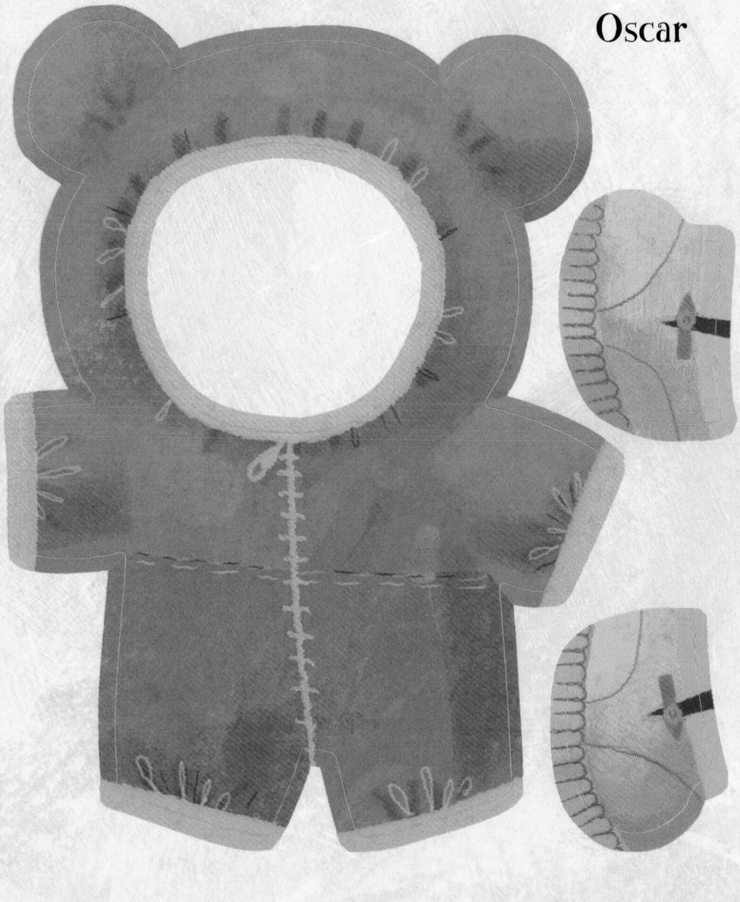

Izzy

Baking cakes

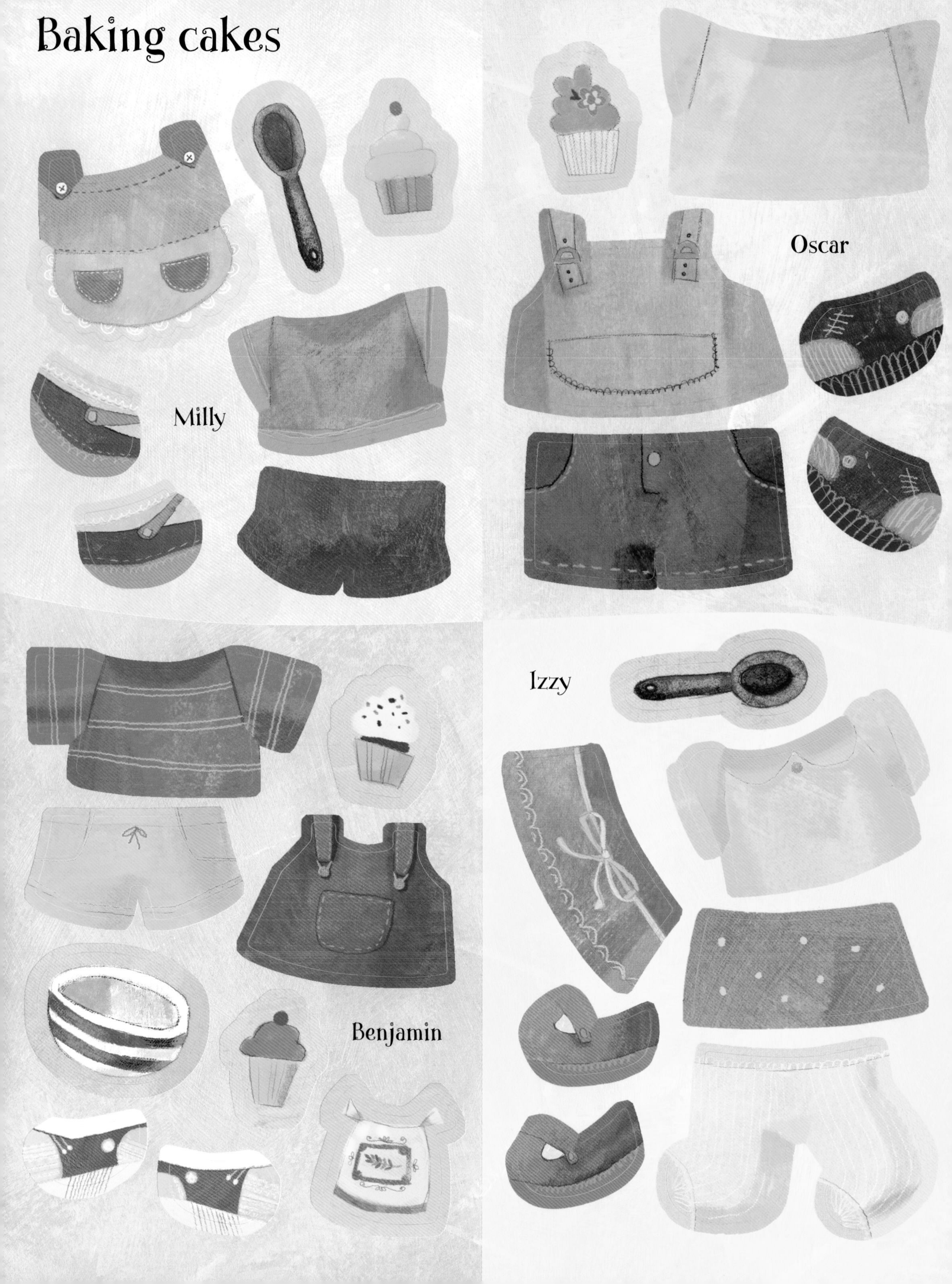

The teddy bears' picnic

Oscar

Izzy

Benjamin

Milly

Playing in the yard

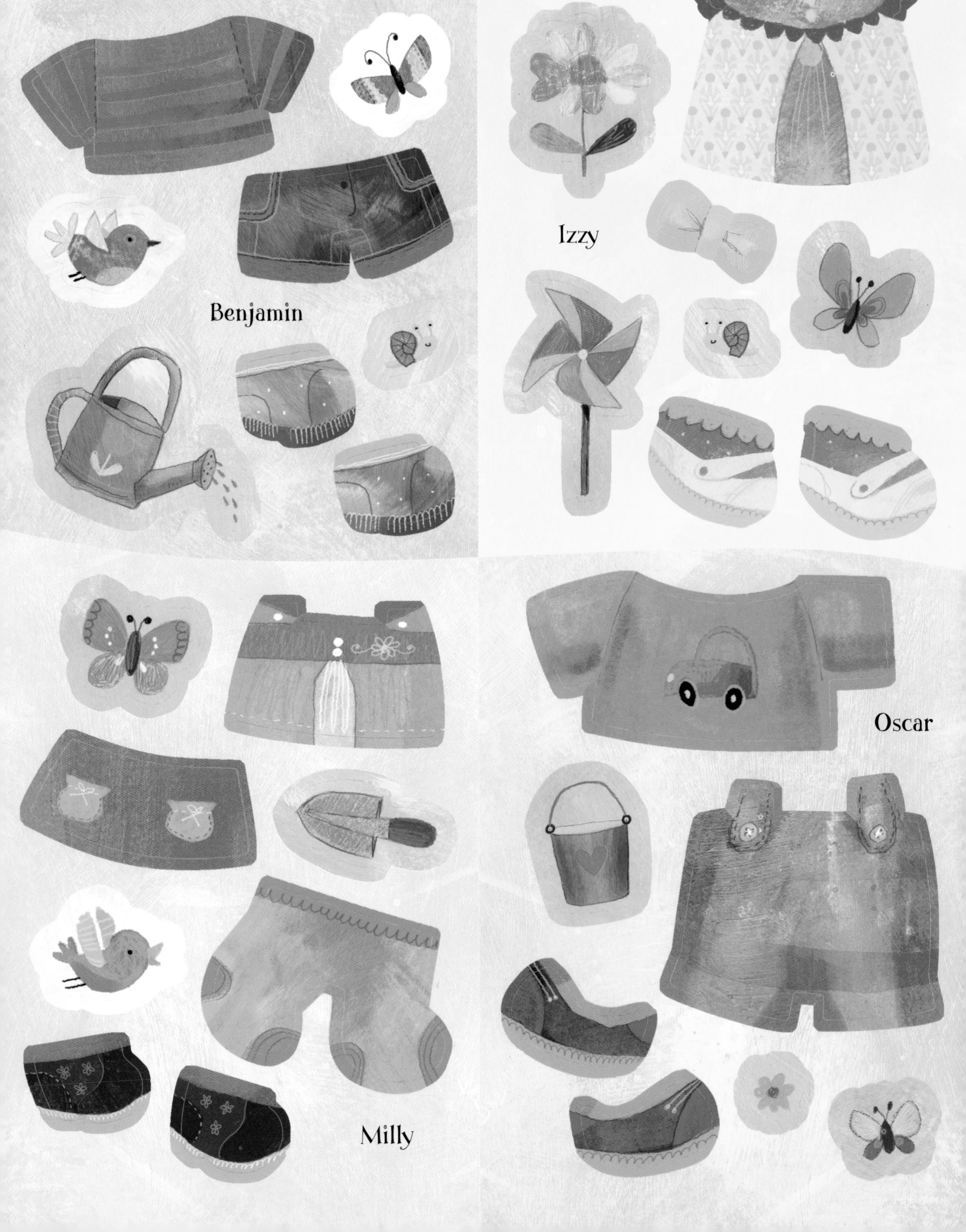

Dress-up fun

Izzy

Benjamin

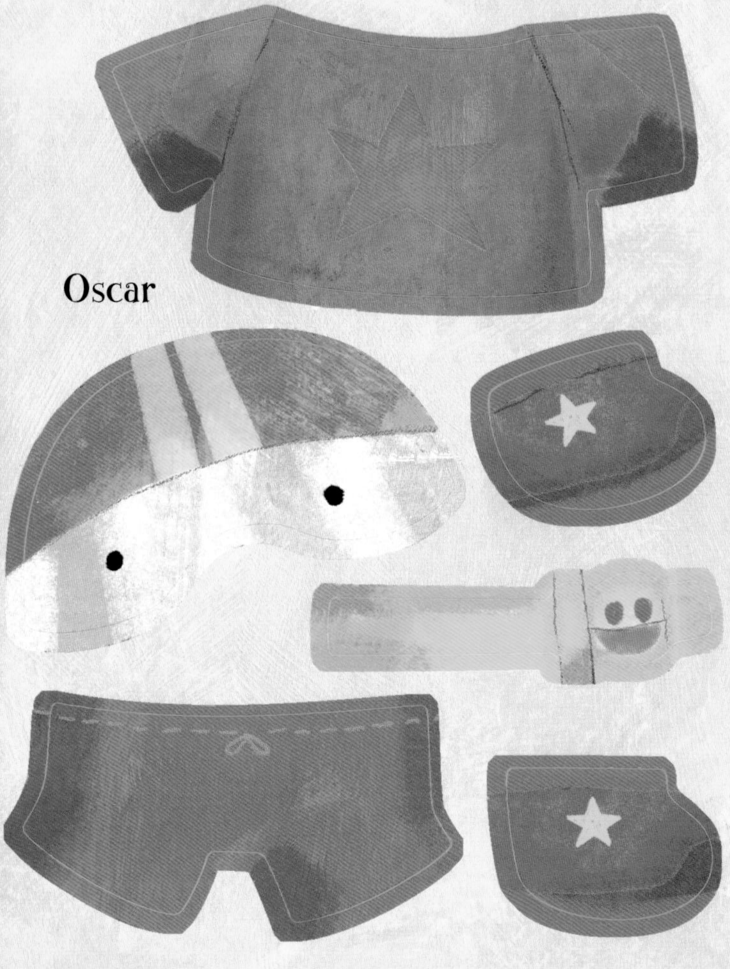

Oscar

Milly

Night-night, bears

Izzy

Benjamin

Milly

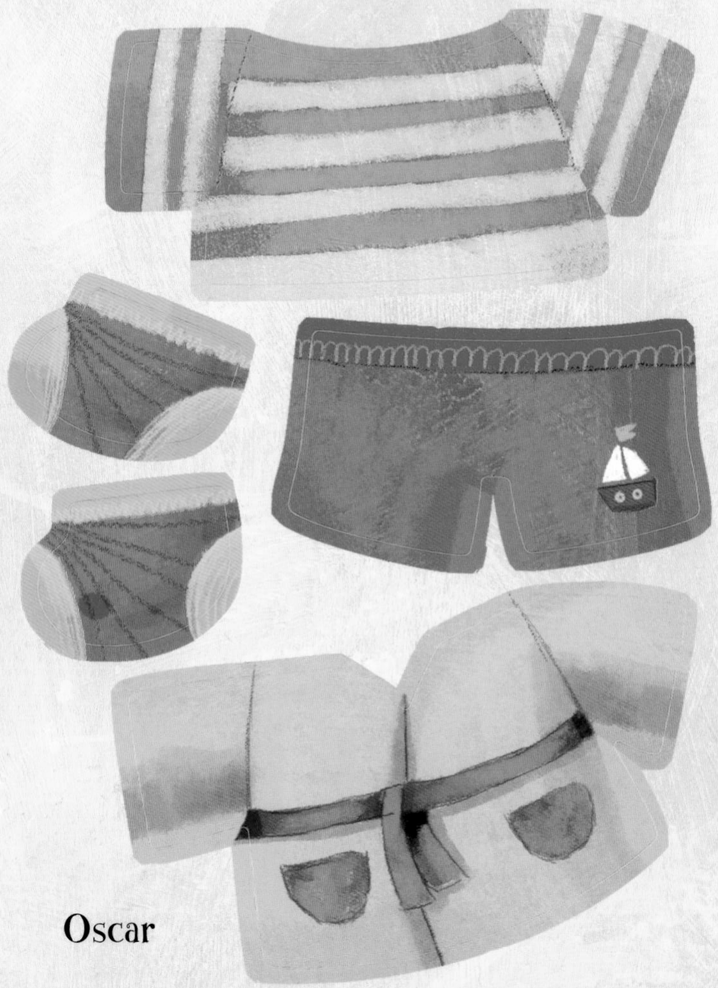

Oscar

Four furry friends

You can put these stickers anywhere you like in the book.

buzzzzzz
I love cupcakes!
flitter, flutter
A juicy red apple for me!

Playing in the yard

After the picnic, the bears go home to play outside. Help them choose some clothes to play in.

tweet
tweet
Let's play!
flitter,
flutter

You can't
catch me!

Dress-up fun

Before bedtime, there's just time to play dress up. Choose some dress-up clothes for each teddy bear.

Arrrrrr! I want to be a pirate.
I want to be a cowgirl.

Weeee!
I'm a super-
hero!

I'm a pretty
pink fairy.

Night-night, bears

After a long, busy day, the teddy bears are very, very tired. Can you help them get ready for bed?

Tick-tock
Tick-tock
Sleep tight!
Goodnight!

Bye-bye!
See you in the morning!

Four furry friends

Add the stickers to finish the pictures of the four teddy bear friends.